Work in the Woods

Looking at the pictures in this book reminded me of my first visit to the Forest in my early teens, when I stayed at Micheldean Youth Hostel on a railway and tramway heritage weekend. I remember seeing an amazing mixture of places and landscapes through the windscreen of a fellow guest's Fiat 500.

Perhaps that is why I felt a special affinity to the Forest when the Countryside Agency chose this area to try out a new approach to rural development – one in which all the relevant agencies work together to secure added value. We are working with the local Regeneration Partnership and Forest communities to make the amazing mixture of landscape and heritage the driving force for regeneration that brings long-term benefits to people and the environment.

One way of making sure this happens is to promote publications such as this, both as a celebration of what is still there to be seen, and as a reminder that this special place needs our commitment, investment and care.

Work in the Woods celebrates the spirit of Dean's industrial heritage, using contemporary photographs. These photographs are the result of Chris Morris's long fascination with the huge diversity and contradictions in the Forest's landscapes. Although present-day images can't convey the scale of industrial development in the Forest at its height, Chris's personal approach to digital photography conveys the spirit of this fascinating local heritage.

Richard Wakeford
Chief Executive, Countryside Agency

Work in the Woods
The Industrial Heritage of Dean

IMAGES AND COMMENTARY BY

Chris Morris

TANNERS YARD PRESS

2002

Thanks to Val Kirby, John Harvey, and everyone in the Forest

First published 2002 by Tanners Yard Press
Church Road, Longhope, Gloucestershire GL17 0LA

© 2002 Chris Morris

Published with the support of The Countryside Agency
Designed and typeset in Galliard by Bookcraft Ltd, Stroud, Gloucestershire
Printed and bound in Great Britain by The Charlesworth Group, Huddersfield, West Yorkshire

British Library Cataloguing in Publication Data
A catalogue record for this book is available from the British Library

ISBN 0–9542096–0–5

'The past isn't dead. It isn't even past' William Faulkner

Historically the Forest of Dean has always been an isolated area, wedged in a narrow V-shape between the rivers Severn and Wye, across which there was very limited access. Isolated but not ignored, as since pre-Roman times its mineral wealth has been explored and exploited.

The short side of the triangle, the Forest's northern edge, is a land of soft low hills with sheep grazing under ragged plum orchards; to the south the ground rapidly steepens, with vantage points giving glimpses of both rivers. Sharp-sided valleys (known locally as slades) run up into the high ridges. Broad-leafed planting screens commercial pines, leaving stone-built settlements as islands in the trees. The decidedly grey aspect of the Forest towns and some of the names on the Forestry signs (Speculation, Union), plus the unmistakable domed shapes of old slag heaps, rearing up with the tree cover, provide the sure signs of the old industry.

Coal and iron have been mined for more than two millennia. Iron diggings have left distinctive rocky gullies and caves, with non-ferrous stone left as standing columns and arches, areas known locally as scowles. Until the eighteenth century, iron smelting used charcoal as the fuel; furnaces were sited in the valley bottoms so water power could be used to drive the bellows.

Through the spread of small-scale coal mining, the tradition evolved, still alive today, of the Forest Freeminers. This is the popular concept of the Forest industry – a one-man band freelancing with a hole in the ground and a corrugated iron lean-to as a store. But a study of early twentieth-century photos reveals this to be only a small part of the story that culminated in industry on a massive scale, with whole wide valley heads covered in buildings and smoking chimneys from skyline to skyline.

Transport and access were an integral part of industrial development. With no bridge across the Severn south of Gloucester, the river, despite its fierce tides and shifting sandbanks, became the commercial highway. Access from the River was by tramway, supplemented and superseded by Brunel's broad gauge railway, which in its turn was reduced to the modern standard. By 1900 the Forest was a myriad network of rail tracks, many of which survive today as cycle routes.

With the coming of steam power the Freeminer became part of a waged labour force. By the end of the nineteenth century new technology led to the deep pits, some with shafts of three hundred metres; economy of scale led small mines to merge (Northern United was a pit, not a football team). Still the merciless financial pressures of the modern world dictated that even these pits would not survive – some were closed in the thirties and the last on Christmas Day 1965.

Ironically the historic misconception has come full circle – today the only coal mining is by half a dozen Freeminers still active in the woods. When the Coal Board relinquished its Forest empire to the Forestry Commission safety concerns, and probably lack of interest, led to widespread demolition (for instance Darkhills Furnace, where Robert Mushet first developed steel, ended up as rubble to be used as foundations for the Severn Bridge); today's attitudes are more caring and various restorations are actively planned.

Despite all the losses there remains, often deep in the woods, a scattering of mine sites, furnaces, tramroads and railway routes with their bridges and tunnels (communications being an essential part of the story) which evoke the spirit if not the scale of the industrial heyday.

Early Days

The early diggings for iron, known as scowles, where non-iron-bearing rock has been left standing as columns, date back to pre-Roman times. This example is at Puzzle Wood, but there are others at Devil's Chapel and Noxon Park. *ABOVE*

The origins and purpose of the Drummer Boy Stone are a pre-historic mystery, but traces of smelted iron have been shown to be in the worn depression on its top surface. *LEFT*

The Dean Road is possibly Roman, suffering a subsequent resurfacing job by less competent workmen. *RIGHT*

Transport

This pack-horse bridge at Soudley, just below the north portal of Bradley Hill Tunnel, defines the earliest route up the valley. *ABOVE*

Tramways, pre-dating the steam railways, were laid directly onto the stones without sleepers. This is the best example, at Bixslade, just up from the stone works. *RIGHT*

The Forest became covered with a myriad network of tramways and railways: this steam locomotive is at Dean Forest Railway. *LEFT*

Bullo Pill and Haie

Bullo was the first Forest harbour, a tiny muddy inlet fitted with tidal gates to the Severn. *RIGHT*

To drive the tramroad from the River at Bullo through to the industry at Soudley the tunnel at Haie was dug, at half a mile reputed to be the longest in the world at the time. Both portals of the tunnel are bricked up. The fence corner made of broad gauge rail is over Haie's west portal – the green swathe beyond leads to Bradley Hill tunnel. *LEFT, ABOVE*

Lydney Harbour

Lydney was built to compete with Bullo as the main port for the Forest industry. A one mile-long linear harbour stretched inland from the Severn, lined with tracks and coal chutes; this is now nothing but a reed-choked canal. However, at the River end, past the abandoned lock gates, the old tidal basin and pier are in working order and due to be restored.

Severn Bridges

The Forest's mineral wealth was valueless without links to the wider world. The Severn Railway Bridge from Sharpness to Purton was built in 1879. It was destroyed in 1960 as two fuel tankers collided with it in fog and exploded; the only remains are the abutments on the east side and the pier for the swing section across the canal. RIGHT

Purton Viaduct is the only remnant of a speculative scheme of 1830 to build a route to a port at Purton Pill, to rival Bullo; there was talk of a 'moving bridge' over the Severn. LEFT

Over had provided the Severn's lowest crossing point since pre-history; Telford's magnificent stone *tour de force* dates from 1827. BELOW

Wye Bridges

This disused railway bridge at Lydbrook is now on the route of the Wye Valley Walk. On the far side, a tunnel under Welsh Bicknor cuts off a huge loop of the route following the river; walkers have voted with their feet by knocking a way through the bricked-up portals. *ABOVE*

Half a mile south-east, a quantity of cut stone from Lydbrook's dismantled viaduct lies dumped in the railway cutting. *LEFT*

The railway bridge at Chepstow is by Brunel, pre-dating his Saltash bridge. Other interesting Wye bridges are Rennie's road bridge at Chepstow and Telford's at Bigsweir. *RIGHT*

Gunns Mill

This seventeenth-century charcoal blast furnace (the dates 1682 and 1683 are cast on lintels) is one of the finest in the country. Latest research shows that the upper part, used in the eighteenth century as a paper mill, was part of the original structure. Whether spelled Guns, Gunn or Gunns, the Mill is not named after the fact that cannons were cast here, but after the original owner, Mr Gunn. English Heritage is actively involved in restoration. *LEFT*

Whitecliff

Coming down the hill from Coleford, the stone buttresses of Whitecliff loom up as if a massive mediaeval castle. This is the best-surviving furnace in the Forest, built by David Mushet for experimental work, burning coke, in 1809, but abandoned by 1820 when he set up Darkhill. *RIGHT*

Three miles to the south, another coke-burning furnace, Oakwood Mill, is a total contrast, a small archway and pile of stones in a placid pony field. *BELOW*

Charcoal

Charcoal-burning with a turf-covered fire now only happens twice a year at the Dean Heritage Centre. The 'drum' method, seen here at Hopes Wood, is the new tradition. Also at the Centre is this wagon from the Wood Distillation Company of Parkend: loaded with timber and wheeled into an oven, the primary purpose was the collection of valuable gases for industrial and military use – charcoal being a mere by-product. *BELOW*

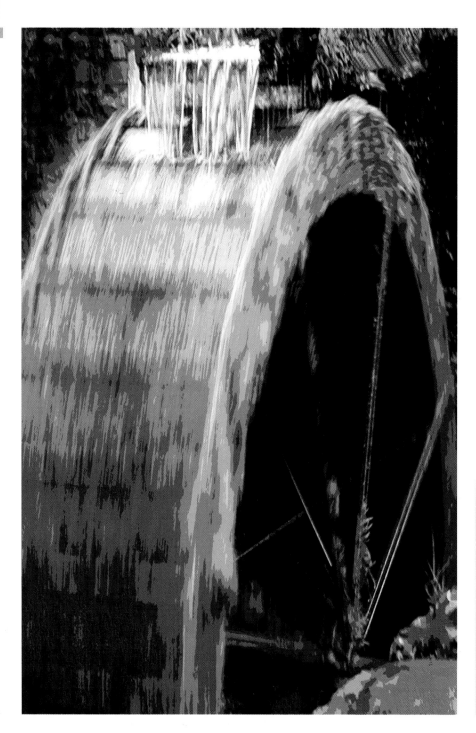

Water in the woods

Water was a blessing and a curse. All the early furnaces and foundries were sited in the valley bottoms to take advantage of water power. This wheel is at Dean Heritage Centre. When steam power came, water was diverted, controlled and collected in ponds, as important as any industrial fuel. *LEFT*

For miners, the risk of flooding was a constant problem which even pumps couldn't always solve. This flood is on a tramway near the Knockley Tunnel. *RIGHT*

Blackpool Brook, seen in a dry autumn, is canalised for a section, with cobbled floor and dry stone walls. *BELOW*

Darkhill and Titanic

David Mushet and his son Robert Forrester moved to Darkhill from Whitecliff in 1820; a plaque, beneath the simple memorial made of rail track, claims that steel was developed here. *RIGHT, BELOW*

Titanic, to the north west of Darkhill, was developed in the 1860s. A century later it was demolished and the rubble used as foundations for the Severn Road Bridge; this ruin in a cottage garden may be a lone survivor. *LEFT*

Fairplay Shaft

This engine house contained an underbeam pumping engine, sited directly over the shaft of a deep iron mine. Forest Enterprise plans a restoration. The name Fairplay Shaft may have an ironic twist: a story claims that this was a Victorian financial scam, raising money to sink the shaft with no real expectation of finding iron. **RIGHT**

Wigpool Iron Mine

Along the ridge from Fairplay, Ken Durham lives in what was the office of the mine where his father worked. Beside him is the 'kibble', the only example of the giant bucket used for raising and lowering men and materials in the shaft. **LEFT**

Lea Bailey Gold Mine

The similarity of the geology here to that of the South African Rand persuaded Boer War widows to invest in a gold mine. Gold was found, but in tiny quantities, and Lea Bailey became an iron ore mine – not surprising in retrospect, as its levels are directly below Wigpool.

Clearwell

Clearwell is a thriving 'visitor centre', showing off its extensive network of caverns left by iron extraction over two millennia. Beyond the public gaze, Ray Wright also mines ochre, a form of ore that is valuable as a pigment, scraping it onto a polythene sheet rather as a Mediterranean peasant shakes ripe olives into a net.

Findall Chimney

This magnificent chimney, high on Staples Edge, is one of the few Forest industrial buildings to have received any restoration. Built to ventilate Perseverance iron ore mine, it includes a grate, enabling a fire at ground level to force a draught up from the working levels below.

Moseley Green

A loop of the Severn and Wye railway tunnelled beneath the Blakeney to Parkend road just south of Moseley Green. The air vent is visible from the Soudley road junction. The tunnel door is open at the north end, but don't be tempted – it is sealed at the south. Just to the west is another small open tunnel on the earlier tramway route.

The Rising Sun

Surrounded by old deep pits and drift mines, this is the Freeminers' pub. The corrugated hut is on an open area known as the Patches, where there are myriad openings and shafts for the Howbeach Levels. *RIGHT*

The winding wheel, the only one remaining in the Forest, was rescued from the pond behind the pub. It belonged to Protheroe's Independent Mine, some of the shafts of which landlord Kevin Howells, who has lived here for nearly fifty years, can point his customers to. *BELOW*

Brick Pits Colliery is a quarter of a mile down the tramway. *LEFT*

Walk in the woods

Whether walking, orienteering or cycling, there are always sights to see. Dilke Bridge is typical of the many spanning the old rail routes that are now cycleways. Other fine examples deep in the woods are at Central and Mierystock.   *RIGHT*

The Knockley Tunnel is one of the few you can walk through.   *LEFT*

Morses Level is an apparently ready-to-go drift mine, and may be inactive due to the Free-miners' dispute over licence fees.   *BELOW LEFT*

Ropehouse Ditch drains marshy land at Sallowvallets, a favourite orienteering terrain.
BELOW RIGHT

Lightmoor

This building is the only surviving winding engine house; the site is used as a timber yard, and there is talk of restoration. The steam engine, now at the Dean Heritage Centre, was originally in a building on this site.

Flour Mill Colliery

This engine house has been restored and is now used to rebuild steam locomotives for private collectors. The tramway approach tunnel from the east is one of the few not bricked up.

Four Deep Pits

The timber frame for a winding wheel on the tip at Parkend Royal is the Forest's only surviving example. *RIGHT*

Speculation is not much more than a picnic site, but this loading wall is 300 metres up the old tramway (not the cycle track). There is a larger loading wall at New Fancy. *ABOVE*

The enigmatic rods emerging from a brick base are at Castlemaine, where the handsome office building is now a private house. *LEFT*

Demolished buildings behind Eastern United adjoin old sidings below Shakemantle Quarry. *ABOVE LEFT*

Princess Royal

The bath house at Princess Royal is a classic building of 1944. Paid for by subscription from the miners' wages, it is to be hoped that European money, available for the re-generation of deep pit sites, will mean renovation, not redevelopment. There are similar bath houses at Cannop, Northern and Eastern, but they are all altered. *LEFT*

Art nouveau tiles line the walls of the washrooms in the abandoned mine offices across the road; the owner aims to make a complete restoration. *RIGHT*

The vent is some way away at Lydney Park. *BELOW LEFT*

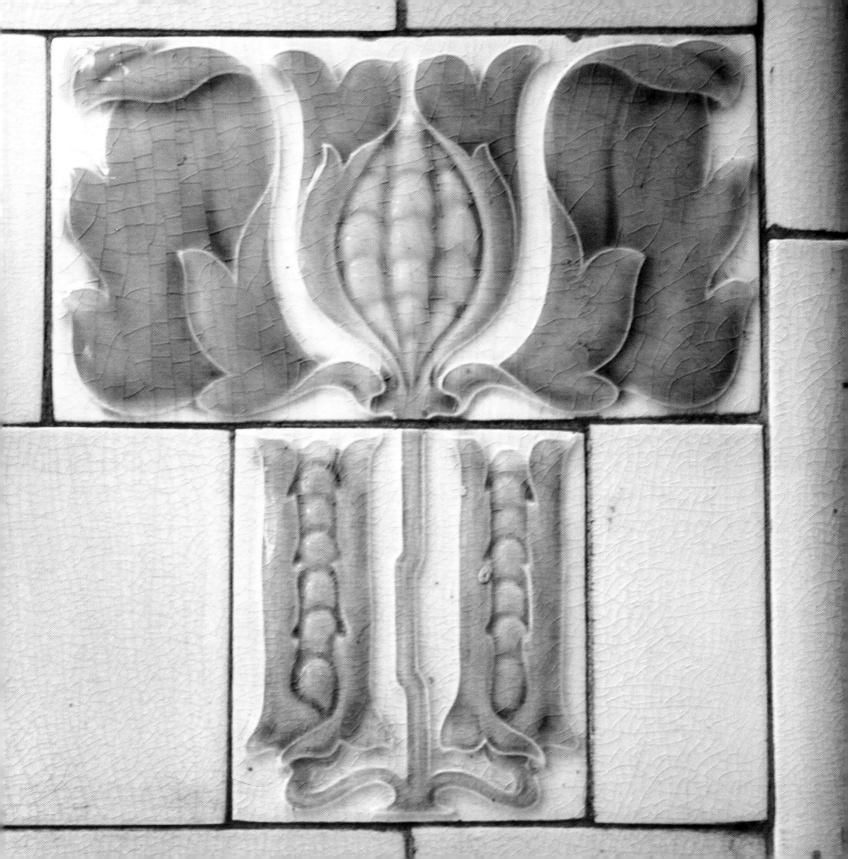

Northern United

The four pits that merged to form Northern included Bowson (page 2), which in 1867 was the Forest's first attempt at deep shaft mining. Northern was the last deep pit to produce coal, closing on Christmas Day, 1965. The buildings are derelict, though in use by a rubbish disposal company. There is little chance of refurbishment as, good news for the community, European money signals a total redevelopment of the site. The distinctive shape of the wooded tip is a landmark by the main Mitcheldean to Monmouth road.

Cannop Colliery

Adjacent to the cycle centre, the buildings of Cannop deep mine are now used as a council depot. The powder magazines remain in splendid isolation in the woods just to the north. *RIGHT*

To the south-west, behind two large wooded tips, is this drift mine entrance; it was used by the miners during the war to save power by not operating the deep shaft cage. *ABOVE*

The sluice gate is on the pond across the road. *LEFT*

Wimberry Slade

The slade climbs into the hill just to the west of the Cannop tips. Cannop drift mine is the only mine to be fenced off and burdened with threatening signs. *RIGHT*

Immediately above, to the north, is Hamblins Yorkley, a drift mine being restored to production capability by a small group led by John Hine; meeting on Tuesday nights, they put in a couple of hours before brewing up, then retiring to the Rising Sun. *LEFT*

The abandoned hut is a further quarter mile up the slade, on the north side. *BELOW*

Quidchurch

Deep in the woods on Staples Edge, this drift mine on the Quidchurch Level seems poised with a fine ambiguity between production and abandonment. In fact Ray Ashley has now joined the new team at Monument Mine.

Lydbrook Deep Level

Mervyn Bradley spent four years actively bringing this drift mine up to Health and Safety standards with a second entrance. In the autumn of 2000 he also moved to Monument Mine.

Monument Mine

Formerly known as Hayners Bailey, Gerald Haynes worked on his own here for three decades before retiring late in 2000.
LEFT AND BACK COVER

This drift mine is still the only one actually producing coal at the time of writing, in the hands of a new team now – Mervyn Bradley, Ray Ashley, and Mervyn's son Mark. *ABOVE*

Close by is the memorial by sculptor Matt Baker, which marks the shaft of Union deep pit, where five men died in an accident in 1902. Commissioned by the Forest Freeminers, it is carved from stone from Mine Train Quarry just up the slade. *PAGE 4*

Hopewell Colliery Museum

The winding wheel and frame that flag you down at this brown sign site may be phony, but Robin Morgan takes visitors down a genuine drift mine; one of the 'roads' has an amazing dry stone arched roof. Robin also mines coal in the nearby Phoenix Level, and is preparing a new entrance, New Road Level, for easier access for future production.

Quarries

Wilderness continues to produce hard red sandstone from its angled beds. *ABOVE LEFT*

Bixslade has a long history: twenty-ton slabs used to travel by tramway down to the stone cutting factory, but now a lorry uses the road. Cast iron shelters provide a refuge from blasting, but today's team, watched over by their Victorian crane, mainly use compressed air drills. *ABOVE, LEFT, RIGHT*

Cannop Stone Firms

For 200 years, stone from the quarry in Bixslade has been cut here, as well as imported granite and Portland stone. The machinery is exactly the same as when driven by steam – the overhead crane had its own steam engine aboard! Corrugated iron, the ubiquitous Forest building material, here reaches its grand climax in the huge factory roof.

Old Cinderford

No photography today can show the scale of the industry that once filled this valley. Still, scattered amongst the modern buildings of the Industrial Estate are visual reminders: Bilson Gas Work, a chemical plant, the brickworks and the scotch derrick of the timber yard at Nailbridge.

Page and grid references to locations shown on the map opposite

69	649139	Bilson Gas Works	30	644195	Lea Bailey Gold Mine
64	597109	Bixslade Quarry	58	606159	Lydbrook Deep Level
9	605099	Bixslade Tramway	18	587177	Lydbrook, Wye Bridge
24	644085	Blackpool Brook	18	595170	Lydbrook Viaduct (north end)
2	645152	Bowson	14	651014	Lydney Harbour
10	664103	Bradley Hill Tunnel (east end)	42	641120	Lightmoor Engine House
46	630084	Brick Pits Colliery	48	616046	Lydney Park Vent
11	670098	Bullo Pill	40	614145	Mirystock Bridge
52	607125	Cannop Colliery	60	604100	Monument Mine
66	607099	Cannop Stone Firms	40	639088	Morses Level
46	619081	Castlemaine	36	631081	Moseley Green
40	627107	Central Bridge	68	647162	Nailbridge
19	539940	Chepstow (Brunel's bridge)	20	596059	Oakwood Mill
32	577082	Clearwell	16	817196	Over Bridge
26	589088	Darkhill Furnace	46	627097	New Fancy
8	628043	Dean Forest Railway	50	637155	Northern United
22, 24, 42	664106	Dean Heritage Centre	6	589066	Noxon Park Scowles
7	652087	Dean Road	46	621083	Parkend Royal
6	604047	Devils Chapel	48	613062	Princess Royal
41	642126	Dilke Bridge	62	605109	Phoenix Level
6	655091	Drummer Boy Stone	16	670049	Purton Viaduct
46	652113	Eastern United	6	517093	Puzzle Wood
29	659165	Fairplay Shaft	56	647104	Quidchurch
34	651105	Findall Chimney	38	631087	Rising Sun
44	604067	Flour Mill Colliery	16	678035	Severn Railway Bridge
20	675159	Gunns Mill	8	661105	Soudley Pack Horse Bridge
10	665102	Haie Tunnel (west end)	46	613138	Speculation
54	602122	Hamblins Yorkley	4	603100	Union
22	683174	Hope Woods	21	568102	Whitecliff Furnace
62	603114	Hopewell Colliery Museum	28	652194	Wigpool
39	640085	Howbeach Levels	64	672185	Wilderness Quarry
40	599083	Knockley Tunnel	54	598122	Wimberry Slade Hut

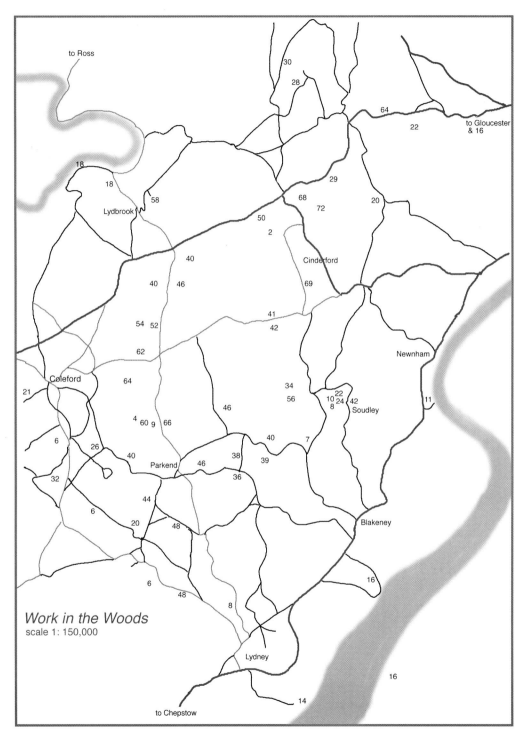

to Ross

30

28

64

22

to Gloucester
& 16

18

18

29

58

68

20

72

50

2

Lydbrook

40

Cinderford

40   46

69

41

42

54 52

62

Newnham

64

34

10 22
24 42
8 Soudley

21

56

Cøleford

46

11

4 60 9 66

40

7

6

26

38

40   39

32

40

Parkend   46   36

44

6

20   48

Blakeney

6

16

48

8

Lydney

16

Work in the Woods
scale 1: 150,000

14

to Chepstow

The index on the left shows all sites referred to in the book, with their page number and grid reference.

The map shows the relationship of the sites: to locate them use Ordnance Survey 1:25 000 map *Outdoor Leisure 14 Wye Valley and Forest of Dean*.

Another useful map is Colin Palmer's map of cycle routes, available from the cycle centre at Cannop.

Many, but not all, of the sites are on land with open access; please respect private property.

Eastern Tip

Nick Bull is one of the team planning to recycle Eastern United's giant tip (north of Findall on Staples Edge) for both stone and coal. Lorries will transport salvaged material to Whitecroft where it will use the Dean Forest Railway to reach Lydney Harbour. Nothing could better exemplify the Forest's ongoing industrial tradition.

Work in the Woods was made possible by using a digital camera; it is tiny, easy to use, has instant reviewing and of course has no film cost. It is not good at capturing action, hence my favouring posed portraits. The second digital benefit is later: many shots were taken in less than ideal light, but the semi-graphic techniques I have used have drawn out the inherent colour and atmosphere of the subjects. I consider these attributes more important than a slavish dedication to conventional photographic quality.

Some purists might groan, but I say this: photography has always used whatever techniques were at its disposal to produce the best possible image. A century ago the aim was to ape reality: but no image is real, only a representation of its subject. Accepting that, it is no further from the truth (as that is the expectation that photographers are burdened with) to tell your story with digital methods than, say, in black and white with all the tricks of the darkroom.

Just as the miners and quarrymen today use coal-cutters and compressed air drills, so photography moves on.